Measure with rods.

about 3 rods long

About how long is

your table?	____ rods
your schoolbag?	____ rods
the cupboard?	____ rods
the sink?	____ rods

Are all carrier bags the same width?

Bag	Width in rods
①	
②	
③	
④	

Which one is widest? _____

3

Measure in feet.

Length of the cupboard	about _____ feet

Length of the table	about _____ feet

Width of the door	about _____ feet

	about _____ feet

Measure in spans.

Length of the cupboard	about _____ spans

Length of the table	about _____ spans

Width of the door	about _____ spans

	about _____ spans

Measure in paces.

About how long is

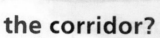

the classroom?	____ paces
the hall?	____ paces
the corridor?	____ paces

Walk 20 paces.

Who walks furthest?

_____

Measure using a long stick.

Length of the classroom	about ____ sticks

Width of the corridor	about ____ sticks

Height of the door	about ____ sticks

Balancing

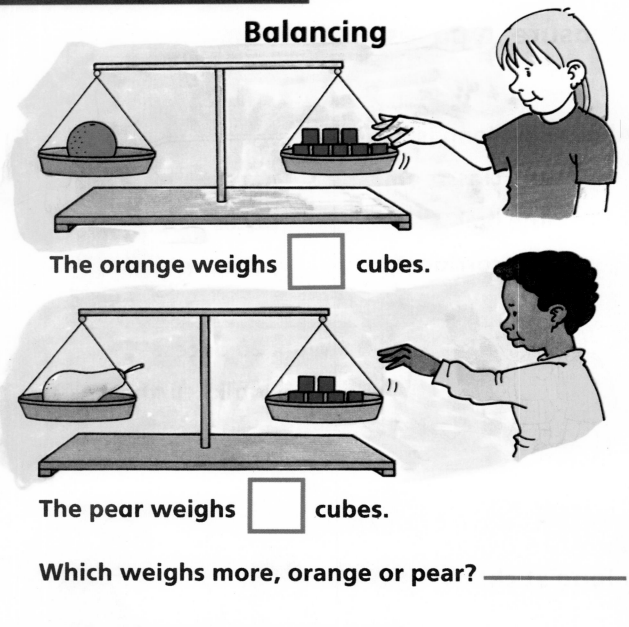

The orange weighs ☐ cubes.

The pear weighs ☐ cubes.

Which weighs more, orange or pear? _____

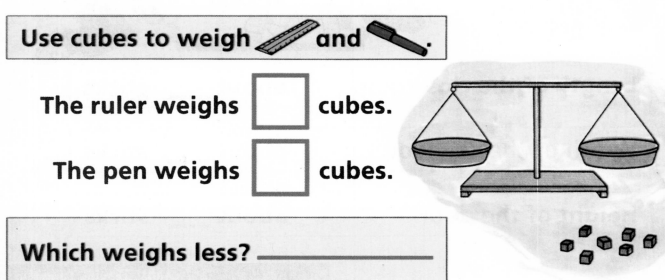

Use cubes to weigh ✏ and 🖊.

The ruler weighs ☐ cubes.

The pen weighs ☐ cubes.

Which weighs less? _____

More balancing

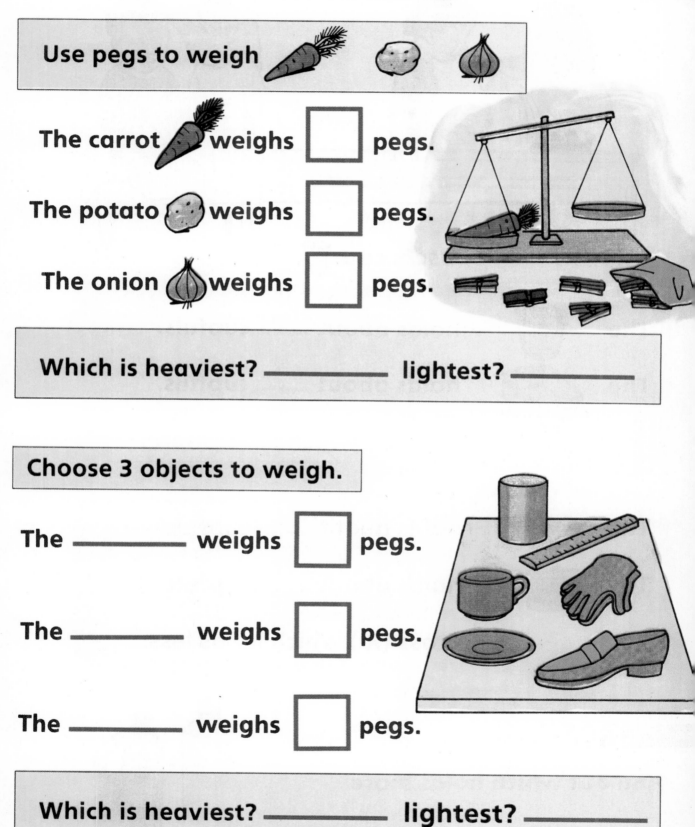

Use pegs to weigh

The carrot weighs ☐ pegs.

The potato weighs ☐ pegs.

The onion weighs ☐ pegs.

Which is heaviest? _____ lightest? _____

Choose 3 objects to weigh.

The _____ weighs ☐ pegs.

The _____ weighs ☐ pegs.

The _____ weighs ☐ pegs.

Which is heaviest? _____ lightest? _____

Cupfuls

Use a cup.

The holds about _____ cupfuls.

The holds about _____ cupfuls.

Tick (✓) which holds more.

The holds about _____ cupfuls.

The holds about _____ cupfuls.

Cross (✗) which holds less.

Find out which holds more.

Ladles and spoons

Use a ladle.

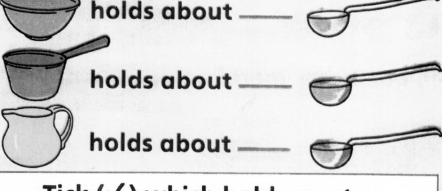

holds about _____

holds about _____

holds about _____

Tick (✓) which holds most.
Cross (✗) which holds least.

Use a spoon.

Find out which holds most.

Pack the boxes.

The ⬤ box holds _____ bricks.

The ⬤ box holds _____ bricks.

Which box holds more? _____

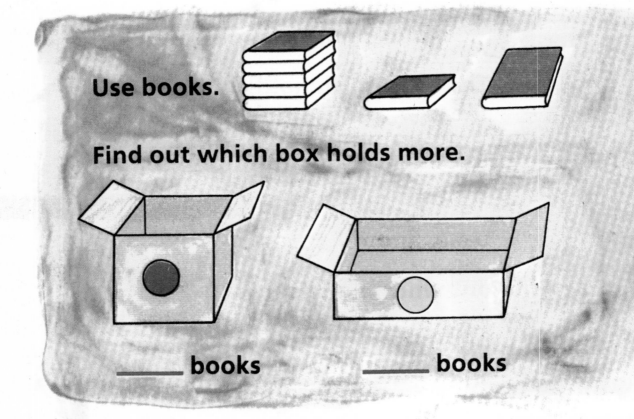

Use books.

Find out which box holds more.

_____ books   _____ books

Sea animals

For each pair, tick (✓) the one with the greater area.

Spotty fish

Use counters to cover each fish with spots.

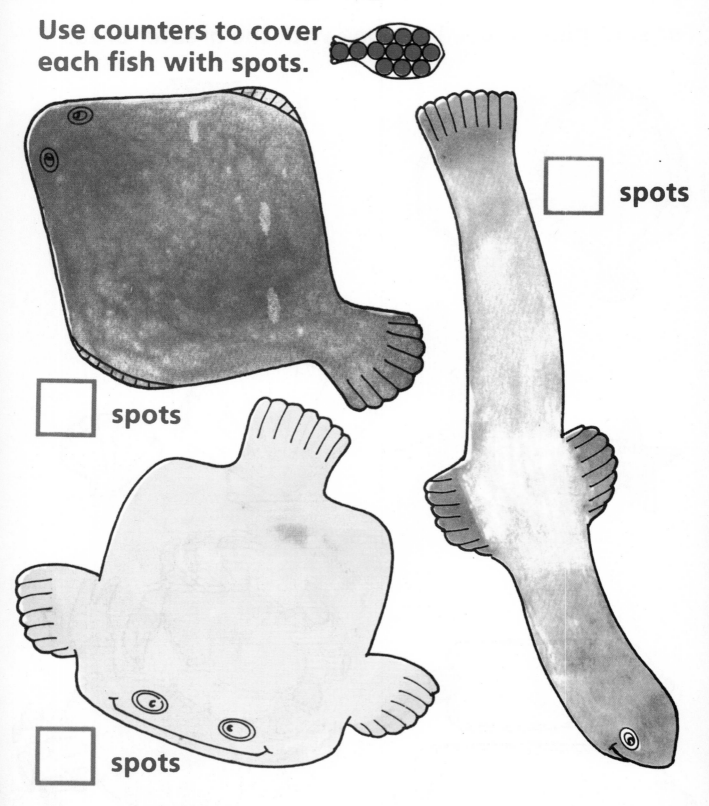

spots

spots

spots

Which fish has the greatest area? _____

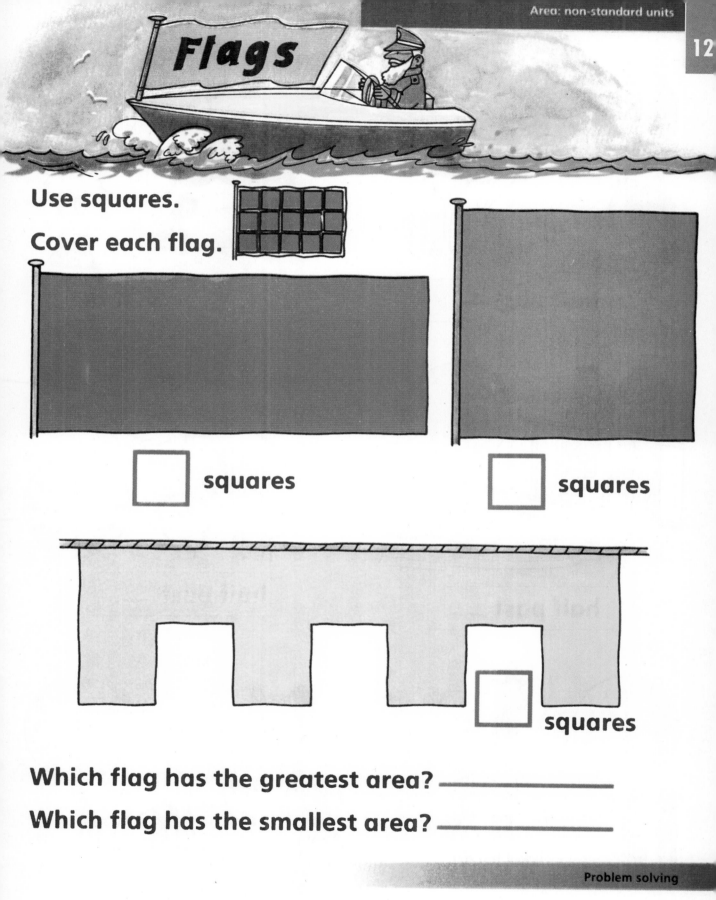

Use squares.

Cover each flag.

[ ] squares

[ ] squares

[ ] squares

Which flag has the greatest area? _____

Which flag has the smallest area? _____

Make a flag with an area of 12 squares.

Safari park

half past

o'clock

half past

half past _____

The is fed at half past 4.

Show this time on a clock.

Colour to match.

half past 5

half past 6

half past 2

12 o'clock

Match

April Fool's Day

New Year's Day

January

February

March

April

May

June

July

August

September

October

November

December

St Valentine's Day

Sports day

My birthday

Summer holidays

Guy Fawkes

Christmas

My friend's birthday

Pat

Monday

Tuesday

Wednesday

Which day?

_____

_____

_____

_____

_____

_____

Problem solving

Which day?

_____

Week ~

| Thursday | Friday | Saturday | Sunday |

Write the missing days.

Monday	_Tuesday_	Wednesday
Thursday	_____	Saturday
Sunday	_____	Tuesday
Tuesday	_____	Thursday
Friday	_____	Sunday
Wednesday	_____	Friday

Today is _____ .

Tomorrow will be _____ .

Yesterday was _____ .

Write the missing words.

| metres | miles | seconds | pints | pounds |

2 _____ of milk, please.

20 _____ to go.

London 20

The baby weighs

8 _____ .

This is the

50 _____ race.

The time taken was

12 _____ .

The giant

Use your hands to measure your height.

My height is about ___ hands.

Talk to your teacher about your heights and about the giant's height.

Cut out the giant's hand.

Could he come into your classroom without bending down?

The giant's hand

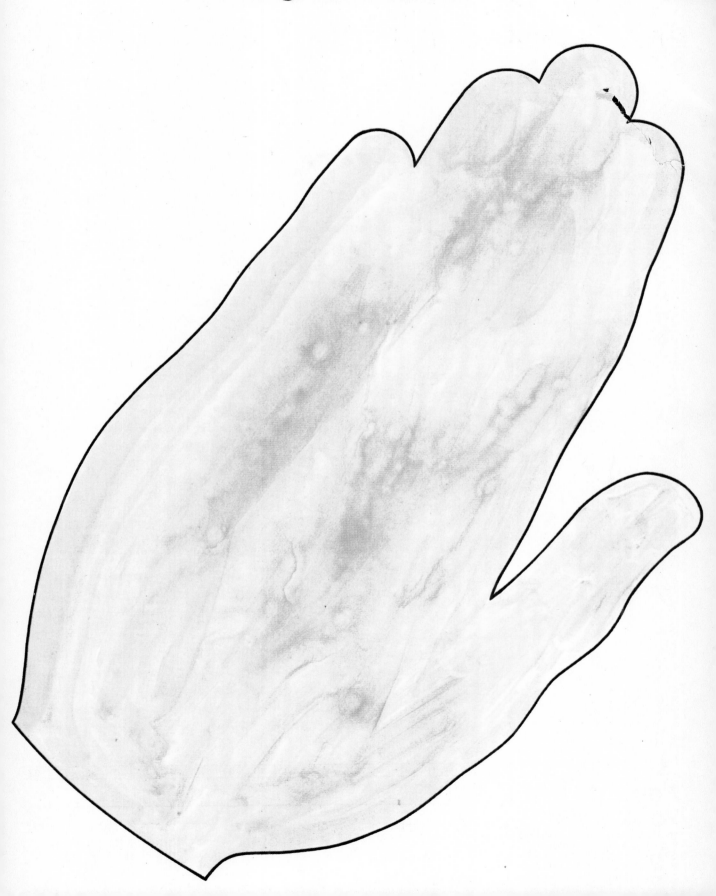

1	2	3	4	5	6	7	8	9	10	11	12	13	14	15	16	17	18	19	20	21	22	23

Heinemann is an imprint of Pearson Education Limited, a company incorporated in England
and Wales, having its registered office at Edinburgh Gate, Harlow, Essex, CM20 2JE.
Registered company number: 872828
ISBN 978 0 435 03095 7 © Scottish Primary Mathematics Group 1981.
First published 1991. Revised edition 1995.   16   22
Typeset and Illustrated by Oxprint Design. Printed and bound in Malaysia (CTP-PJB)

ISBN 978-0-435030-95-7